Grammy Do...

By Sandy Richards

Illustrated by Lori Hohmann

Illustrations by Lori Hohmann

Cover Design by Phillip Gessert (gessertbooks.com)
Book formatted for print and ebook by Phillip Gessert (gessertbooks.com)

Printed in the United States of America

First Printing, 2016

ISBN-10: 0-9981048-1-7
ISBN-13: 978-0-9981048-1-2

TYTIN Publishing
Commerce, MI 48382

www.sandy-richards.com.

Dedication

In loving memory of "Big Mommy" Nora Combs and "Granny" Wilma Jean Little…two beautiful women who set the bar high for all grandmothers. To "Grammy" Sonja Berry…my inspiration. To my grandchildren, Megan, Ben, Olivia, Sam, Lily and Veda…you stole my heart from the moment we met. To my angel Tyler…oh, how I would have spoiled your kids. To my amazing son, Austin…I'm waiting patiently to kiss and cuddle your babies and be their Grammy too!

I will love you all…forever and a day.

Grammy Do...

"I loved this book! Great story and the illustrations are adorable. I think Sandy describes the relationship that so many grandmothers and grandchildren have with one another; heartwarming, so full of love, and a relationship like no other!"

—*Gerry Zarb, "Grandma" to fifteen and "GiGi" to fifteen great-grandchildren*

"I read this book to three of my five grandchildren. They loved it and were amazed that other Nanas do these things too! My three-year-old granddaughter giggled and giggled every time we said Grammy Do! It was a real hit."

—*Darlene Gilbert, "Nana" to fifteen grandchildren*

"*Grammy Do*...excellently portrays the special sacrificial love and bond that a grandmother has for her grandchildren. Reading this book filled my heart with joy as it brought back so many special memories that I have shared with my grandchildren. This book can be a wonderful conversation starter with your grandchildren as you reflect on your own personal memories."

—*Linda Svacha, "MeMaw" to eight grandchildren*

Who takes my hand when we cross the street?

Who giggles when she sniffs my stinky feet?

Who carries me to bed when I'm fast asleep?

Grammy do...

Who kisses my face with sloppy smooches?

Who allows me to play with her furry pooches?

Who swings me so high that my hair whooshes?

Grammy do...

Who watches me run and jump in puddles?

Who gives me a bath with duckies and bubbles?

Who reads to me in arms full of cuddles?

Grammy do...

Who hands me a bite of a yummy cupcake?

Who shares some sips of her creamy milkshake?

Who claps when I catch fluffy snowflakes?

Grammy do...

Who teaches me tricks to throw a tea party?

Who whips out the crayons when I'm feeling arty?

Who taps my nose and calls me smarty?

Grammy do...

Who sheds a tear when I wave good-bye?

Who says with smile, "just give it a try"?

Who has all the answers when I always ask "why"?

Grammy do...

Who teaches me to sing and sway?

Who gets on her knees with me to pray?

Who tells me she loves me forever and a day?

Grammy do...

"Sandy Richards has captured the essence of what it means to be a "Grammy". Experiencing the joys of sharing life with your grandchildren are some of the most precious memories we can make. I loved reading her book and look forward to sharing it with my grandchildren!"

—*Cheryl Maki, "Nana" to eleven grandchildren*

"A sweet book written straight from the heart, recognizing the beauty of the little things in life that show pure love. Beautifully simplistic, it spells out the love a Grammy pours out to her grandchild. Don't miss reading this beautifully written and illustrated work of art.

—*Kathy Morley, "Grammy Kathy (aka Graham Cracker)" to eight grandchildren*

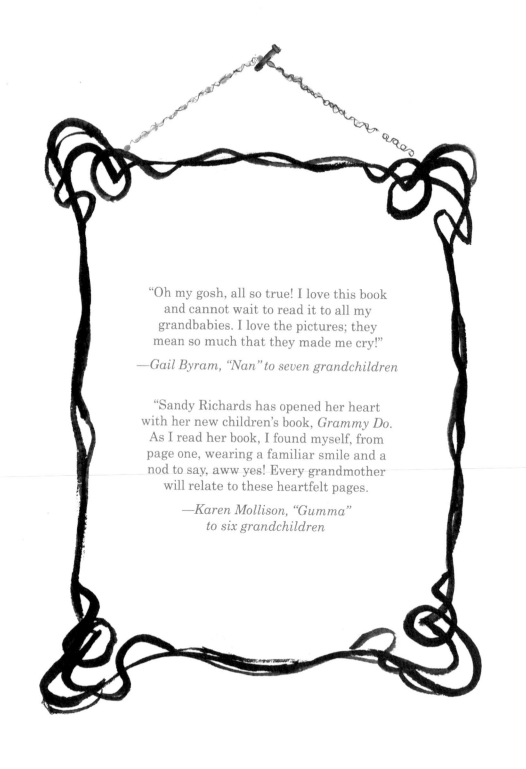

"Oh my gosh, all so true! I love this book
and cannot wait to read it to all my
grandbabies. I love the pictures; they
mean so much that they made me cry!"

—*Gail Byram, "Nan" to seven grandchildren*

"Sandy Richards has opened her heart
with her new children's book, *Grammy Do*.
As I read her book, I found myself, from
page one, wearing a familiar smile and a
nod to say, aww yes! Every grandmother
will relate to these heartfelt pages.

—*Karen Mollison, "Gumma"*
to six grandchildren

f *www.facebook.com/AuthorSandyRichards*

f *www.facebook.com/AFarCryFromHome*

p *www.pinterest.com/AFarCryFromHome*

◉ *www.Sandy-Richards.com*

Made in the USA
San Bernardino, CA
09 May 2018